Antonio VIVALDI

(1678 – 1741)

Concerto for Violin, Strings and Basso continuo
Op. 3 No. 6, RV 356
A minor / la mineur / a-moll

Edited by
Alexandra Ruth Rappitsch

DOWANI International

Preface

This edition presents you with a piece which belongs in the repertoire of every violin pupil: the Concerto for Violin, Strings and Basso continuo Op. 3 No. 6, RV 356 in A minor by Antonio Vivaldi. Our edition enables you to learn this piece systematically and in three differing tempi with professional accompaniments. This edition has been revised and includes a piano reduction and a new solo part with fingerings. The fingerings and bowings in this edition are those of Alexandra Ruth Rappitsch, who, after having studied in Vienna and New York, is currently professor at the Vorarlberger Landeskonservatorium in Feldkirch (Austria). Her pupils have won numerous competitions in Belgium, Germany, Italy and Austria, and have performed in concerts in Graz, Toronto, Venice and Vienna.

The CD opens with the concert version of each movement (violin and orchestra). After tuning your instrument (Track 1), the musical work can begin. First, you will hear the piano accompaniment at slow and medium tempo for practice purposes. At slow tempo you can also hear the violin played softly in the background as a guide. Having mastered these levels, you can now play with orchestra at the original tempo. Each movement has been sensibly divided into subsections for practice purposes. You can select the subsection you want using the track numbers indicated in the solo part. All of the versions were recorded live. The names of the musicians are listed on the last page of this volume; further information can be found in the Internet at www.dowani.com.

We wish you lots of fun playing from our *DOWANI 3 Tempi Play Along* editions and hope that your musicality and diligence will enable you to play the concert version as soon as possible. Our goal is to provide the essential conditions you need for effective practicing through motivation, enjoyment and fun.

Your DOWANI Team

Avant-propos

Cette édition vous présente un morceau qui fait partie du répertoire standard de tous les élèves de violon : le concerto pour violon, cordes et basse continue, op. 3 n° 6, RV 356 en la mineur d'Antonio Vivaldi. Notre édition vous permet de travailler l'œuvre de manière systématique dans trois tempos différents avec un accompagnement professionnel. Il s'agit d'une nouvelle édition révisée avec réduction pour piano et une nouvelle partie soliste avec doigtés. Les doigtés et coups d'archet de cette édition ont été préparés par Alexandra Ruth Rappitsch, professeur de violon qui a fait ses études à Vienne et à New York et qui enseigne au Conservatoire du Vorarlberg à Feldkirch (Autriche). Ses élèves ont gagné de nombreux concours en Belgique, Allemagne, Italie et en Autriche et se sont produits lors de concerts à Graz, New York, Toronto, Venise et Vienne.

Le CD vous permettra d'entendre d'abord la version de concert de chaque mouvement (violon et orchestre). Après avoir accordé votre instrument (plage n° 1), vous pourrez commencer le travail musical. Pour travailler le morceau au tempo lent et au tempo moyen, vous entendrez l'accompagnement de piano. Au tempo lent, le violon restera cependant toujours audible très doucement à l'arrière-plan. Vous pourrez ensuite jouer le tempo original avec accompagnement d'orchestre. Chaque mouvement a été judicieusement divisé en sections pour faciliter le travail. Vous pouvez sélectionner ces sections à l'aide des numéros de plages indiqués dans la partie du soliste. Toutes les versions ont été enregistrées en direct. Vous trouverez les noms des artistes qui ont participé aux enregistrements sur la dernière page de cette édition ; pour obtenir plus de renseignements, veuillez consulter notre site Internet : www.dowani.com.

Nous vous souhaitons beaucoup de plaisir à faire de la musique avec la collection *DOWANI 3 Tempi Play Along* et nous espérons que votre musicalité et votre assiduité vous amèneront rapidement à la version de concert. Notre but est de vous offrir les bases nécessaires pour un travail efficace par la motivation et le plaisir.

Les Éditions DOWANI

Vorwort

Mit dieser Ausgabe präsentieren wir Ihnen ein Stück, das zum Standardrepertoire eines jeden Geigenschülers zählt: das Konzert für Violine, Streicher und Basso continuo op. 3 Nr. 6, RV 356 in a-moll von Antonio Vivaldi. Unsere Ausgabe ermöglicht es Ihnen, das Werk systematisch und in drei verschiedenen Tempi mit professioneller Begleitung zu erarbeiten. Es handelt sich um eine revidierte Neuausgabe mit Klavierauszug und einer neuen Solostimme mit Fingersätzen. Die Fingersätze und Striche in dieser Ausgabe stammen von der erfolgreichen Violinpädagogin Alexandra Ruth Rappitsch, die in Wien und New York studierte und heute als Professorin am Vorarlberger Landeskonservatorium in Feldkirch (Österreich) tätig ist. Ihre Schüler haben zahlreiche Wettbewerbe in Belgien, Deutschland, Italien und Österreich gewonnen und traten bei Konzerten in Graz, New York, Toronto, Venedig und Wien auf.

Auf der CD können Sie zuerst die Konzertversion (Violine und Orchester) eines jeden Satzes anhören. Nach dem Stimmen Ihres Instrumentes (Track 1) kann die musikalische Arbeit beginnen. Zum Üben folgt nun im langsamen und mittleren Tempo die Klavierbegleitung, wobei im langsamen Tempo die Violine als Orientierung leise im Hintergrund zu hören ist. Anschließend können Sie sich im Originaltempo vom Orchester begleiten lassen. Jeder Satz wurde in sinnvolle Übe-Abschnitte unterteilt. Diese können Sie mit Hilfe der in der Solostimme angegebenen Track-Nummern auswählen. Alle eingespielten Versionen wurden live aufgenommen. Die Namen der Künstler finden Sie auf der letzten Seite dieser Ausgabe; ausführlichere Informationen können Sie im Internet unter www.dowani.com nachlesen.

Wir wünschen Ihnen viel Spaß beim Musizieren mit unseren *DOWANI 3 Tempi Play Along*-Ausgaben und hoffen, dass Ihre Musikalität und Ihr Fleiß Sie möglichst bald bis zur Konzertversion führen werden. Unser Ziel ist es, Ihnen durch Motivation, Freude und Spaß die notwendigen Voraussetzungen für effektives Üben zu schaffen.

Ihr DOWANI Team

Concerto

for Violin, Strings and Basso continuo, Op. 3 No. 6, RV 356
A minor / la mineur / a-moll

A. Vivaldi (1678 – 1741)
Piano Reduction: G. Stöver

DOW 4528

Concerto

for Violin, Strings and Basso continuo, Op. 3 No. 6, RV 356

A minor / la mineur / a-moll

I ②

A. Vivaldi (1678 – 1741)
Edited by A. R. Rappitsch

DOW 4528

9

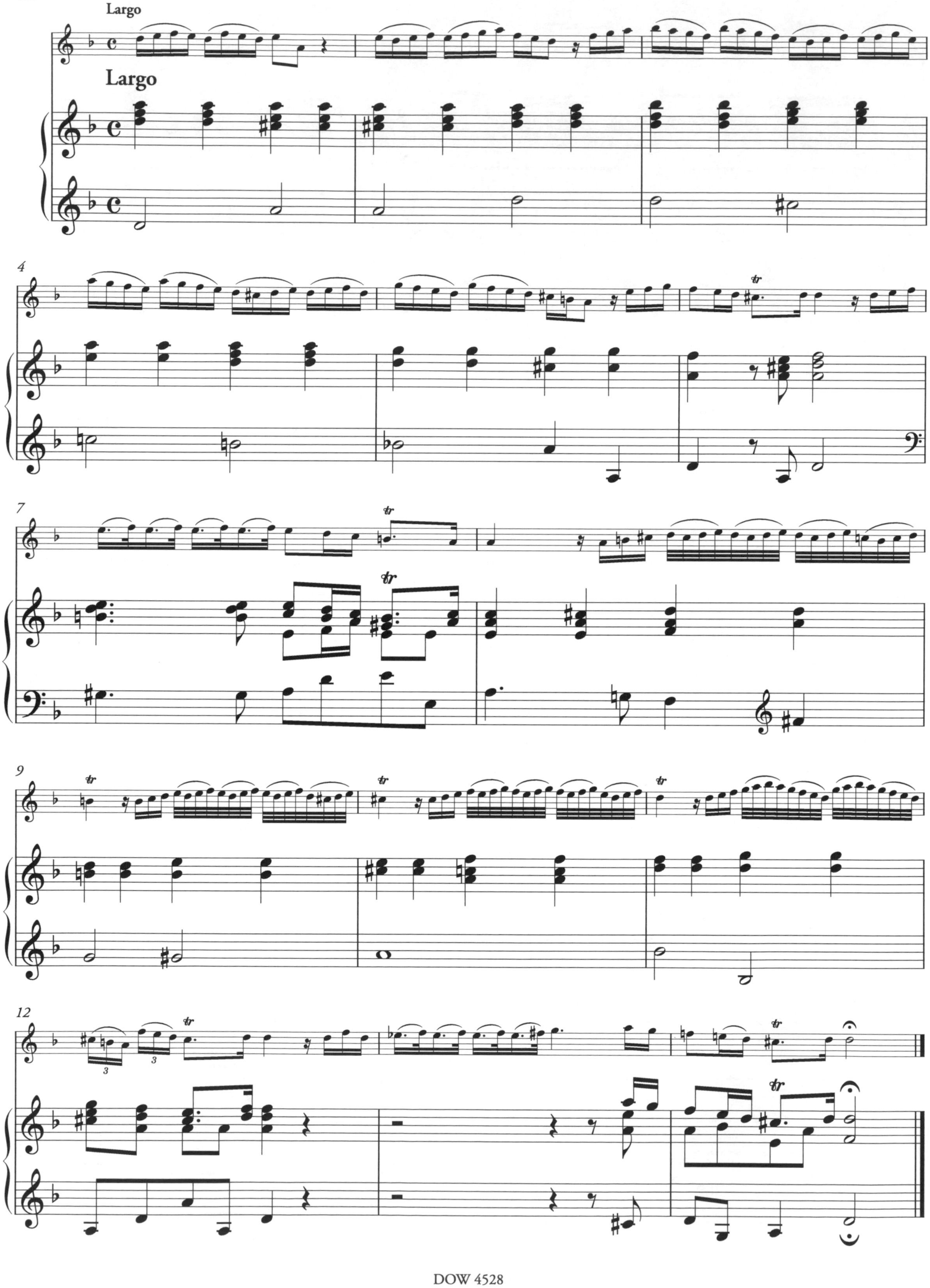
Largo
Largo

DOWANI - 3 Tempi Play Along is an imprint of:
De Haske (International) GmbH
Postfach 60, CH-6332 Hagendorn
Switzerland
Phone: +41-(0)41-784 30 84 / Fax: +41-(0)41-784 30 80
Email: info@dowani.com
www.dowani.com

Recording: Pavel Lavrenenkov, Russia
Digital Mastering: Traton GmbH, Switzerland
Project Supervisor: DraDoVision Est., Drazen Domjanic, Liechtenstein (www.dradovision.com)

Concert Version
Alexey Bruni, Violin
Russian Philharmonic Orchestra Moscow
Konstantin Krimets, Conductor

3 Tempi Accompaniment
Slow:
Leonid Ogrintschuk, Piano

Intermediate:
Leonid Ogrintschuk, Piano

Original:
Russian Philharmonic Orchestra Moscow
Konstantin Krimets, Conductor